WRONGBOY'S

HISTORY OF EARTH

An Inaccurate History of Evolution

OTHER TITLES
made up
by the same author

An Inaccurate History of Evolution

Wrongboy's Book of Executive Chimps

The Erratic Review

The Children's book of Spoiled Paper.

The False Ears of the Long-Eared Owl and Related Phenomena

A Brief History of Tim

A Timed History of Briefs

The Bumper Book of Actual Facts

Milking the Aphid: an ill-researched history of the ant

The Big Bang and its Municipal Heritage

Fish Offering and the Rituals of the Crested Grebe

The Childrens Book of Lies and Inaccuracies

published by Walker Books Ltd 2004

Text and artwork previously owned by
Wrongboy Associate Productions,
A made up Company of Great Britain.

A CIP catalogue record for this book is available from
the British Library

ISBN 0-7445-8644-5

First Published in Great Britain by
Walker Books Ltd 2004
Papers used by Walker Books are natural, recyclable
products made from wood, which are squashed into flat
sheets, onto which ink is applied. Parents should be
aware this Book is not suitable for small children as
it may constitute a choking hazard.

WRONGBOY'S

HISTORY
OF
EARTH

by

Will Bishop-Stephens

PREFACE

Hello Dear Reader,

People often ask me, how do I know so much about
the beginnings of the universe?
How did I come to have such an encyclopaedic
knowledge of the Natural World?

"Well," I say, "there are many ways in which the
bucket collects water, or the humble duck gathers
the grain, and the way that nature reveals itself
is indeed a mysterious thing"
And the People reply, "What have buckets and ducks
got to do with anything. What about research?"

And I tell them, "If Mankind relied only on the
existing knowledge of others…Why that would make
us as the foolish Gadfly who, knowing no better,
does as its forebears have always done, and flies
around in complicated circles for 24 hours before
suddenly dying."
And the People, obviously impressed, shake their
heads in wonder, saying 'I honestly have no idea
what you're talking about."

And so Dear Reader, it is in an effort to pass on my wealth of knowledge that I am composing this book today, in the hope of forming a foundation on which can be built a unifying theory of all Life on Earth.

And all Life in Sea.

And all Life up Tree.

That
and the need to make a Million Pounds quickly.

CONTENTS

Chapter I.

The Dawn of Time

BUT THEN...rabbits etc.

Evolution explained by a qualified scientist

The Age of the Newt

When Mice Ruled the Earth.

The Mammal Explained

The Pinnacle of Evolution....   the elephant

A Groundbreaking Scientific Mime Act.

A Regretable incident at the Ministry.

The History of Man and Cheese.

~~The Evolution of the Machine.~~

The Weather

The Evolution of the Machine;

        The Evolution of Design.

        Early Electrical Life.

        The Age of the Crane.

Wrongboy's World of Tommorrow,

        an exciting tale
        soon to be made into a Hollywood Sci-fi B-Movie

Time Travel.

Space Travel.

The Meaning of Life Itself.

Compendium of Actual Facts... an A-Z of Life on Ear th.

Chapter 1

THE DAWN OF TIME

So here we are at the Dawn of Time itself...

The Dawn of Time forms part of a period known as The
Olden Days.
It was populated by interesting Historical Figures, like
King Henry the Eighth and the Sabre-Toothed Leopard.

What is known of this era comes largely from Fossil
Records, which where kept by the Victorians and the more
educated Dinosaurs.

But by all accounts the Earth was a very different place
at the dawn of time, ~~5 years~~ one hundred thousand million
years ago...

The Youthful Earth was very hot and very poisonous, and
everyone was very disappointed. The Dinosaurs made a lot
of grumbly noises, and the Victorians wrote stern letters
of complaint, but it turned out nothing could be done.

Everything was in a terrible state of higgledy-piggledy,
and the Romans, who liked organising things, marched
everywhere putting things into neat lines that collapsed
as soon as they left.

fig. 1. It is the dawn of time, 5 years ago,

and the Victorians are discussing Plant design.

Meanwhile on the other side of the planet,

a dinosaur is trying to eat the moon.

(again)

AND THEN...

And then, it rained for 40 days and 40 nights, and there was a man called Noah and a boat for fitting everything in called the ark

And the ark was full of dinosaurs,

and everyone got thoroughly depressed.

<u>BUT THEN</u>

<u>But then</u> a number of marvellous things happened,
Romans introduced rabbits, Hamsters discovered
North America and, most importantly, Darwin
invented Evolution.
Darwin's revolutionary discovery was ultimately to
prove too much for the Dinosaurs, and they went to
go and live inside mountains, to sit there for all
time, grumbling and
recalling past glories.

Nobody missed the dinosaurs very much, because
although they looked very impressive, they were
also incredibly stupid and had made themselves
unpopular by trying to unscrew

the head of anyone who tried

to make friends with them

Evolution.

Evolution is very important and looks like this:

Without Evolution we would not have many of the things we hold dear today, such as scented candles, radio advertising and the cosmetic injection of Botulism into ladies' faces.

However,
the way humble Newts turned into elaborate creatures such as the Walrus or the Sausage Dog is very complicated, and the issue of what came befor Newts is so complicated that it can only be explained by a qualified scientist.

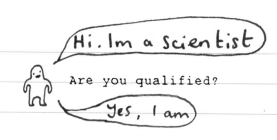

Hi. Im a scientist

Are you qualified?

Yes, I am

Right then, off you go.

Well, the thing about Evolution and the History of the Earth is that the time-scales involved are so huge that they are impossible to conceive of.

People like to compare the 4½ billion year history of Earth to the life span of a 45 year old man

but I dont. I think things like that are rubbish... I mean, you end up with a hot and poisonous middle aged man who suddenly sprouts Animals, its Ludicrous.

Are you sure you're a qualified scientist?

THE AGE OF THE NEWT

"But," I hear you ask, "What about the Newts? How did they come to begin all life on Earth? Are they truly the best animal at splapping about in puddles?"

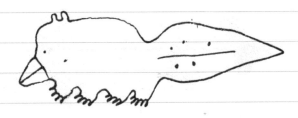

Fig.3.1 The Common Newt.

Newts are universally acknowledged by the scientific community to be the best because their fingers are small and spabbley, and during the early part of the

…Hold on… That's not a Newt…
That's a Small Mouse
in a Newt Costume…

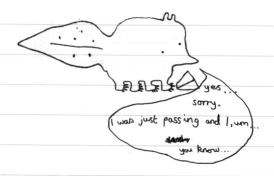

yes...

sorry.

I was just passing and I, um...

~~you~~ you know...

Right...

Anyway.

Newts are the modern version of the creature who
first invented hands. Indeed there was a time when
everyone who wasn't a fish had hands just as moist
and sploinky as the Modern Newt, if not
sploinkier.

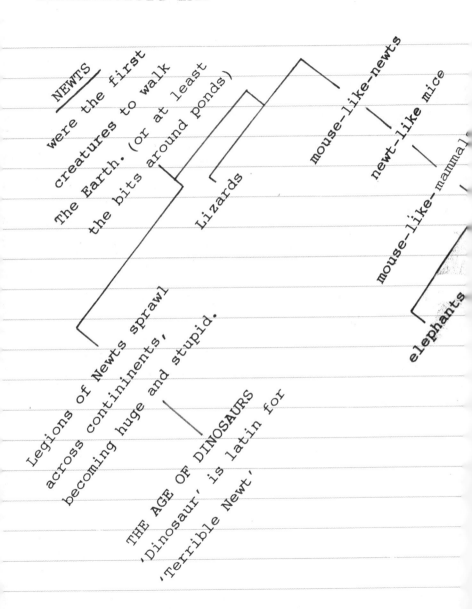

PALAEOEOZOIC ERA

CAENOCZQIC ERA

NEWTS were the first creatures to walk The Earth. (or at least the bits around ponds)

Lizards

mouse-like-newts

newt-like mice

mouse-like-mammal

mouse-like-mammal

elephants

Legions of Newts sprawl across contininents, becoming huge and stupid.

THE AGE OF DINOSAURS 'Dinosaur' is latin for 'Terrible Newt'.

MESOZOIC ERA   MODERN ERA

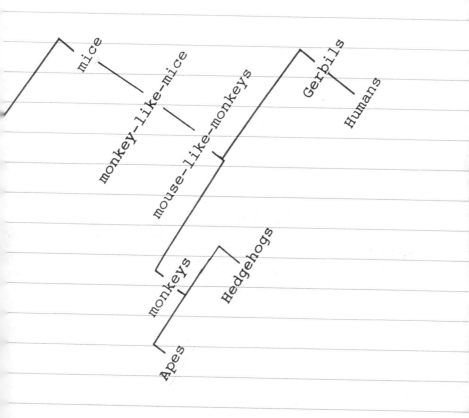

mice

monkey-like-mice

mouse-like-monkeys

Gerbils

Humans

monkeys

Hedgehogs

Apes

Triturus Vulgaris

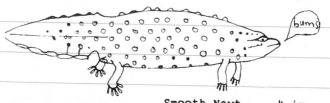

bums

Smooth Newt   4 in.

WHEN MICE RULED THE EARTH

Throughout the Age of the Dinosaurs, which ended
quite abruptly, any animal that fell in between
being a) a large psychotic carnivore
   or b) too small to bother with,
got their head unscrewed from their body
by insane reptiles.

For this reason during this era all mammals were
small inconspicuous hairy creatures

There were still many ferocious reptiles around at this time, threatening the dominance of the Mammals.

But most of them were the size of a kidney bean,

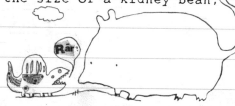

so that was all right.

This woeful lack of competition meant Mouse-like Mammals were able to Dominate the Earth and invent many electrical goods.

AND SO…

And so small furry animals were free to roam the Earth in Majestic Herds, stuffing berries into their expandable cheek pouches.

For they were a Noble Breed-
Fearless, Proud and Fluffy.

Who are you?

oh no.

THE MAMMAL

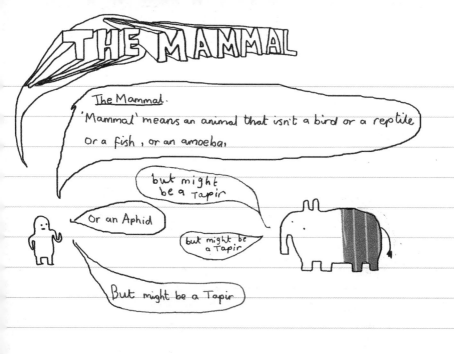

The Mammal.

'Mammal' means an animal that isn't a bird or a reptile or a fish, or an amoeba.

Or an Aphid

but might be a Tapir

but might be a Tapir

But might be a Tapir

Mammals are warm-blooded hairy things and they feed their young out of milk dispensers on their fronts.

I Think they are called Teats

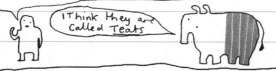

Most Mammals give birth to small squeaky versions of themselves

There are only two exceptions to this rule the spiny Anteaters and the Duck Billed Platypus.

hello

HI

?

ODDITIES

These two creatures form an odd subgroup, because they're very mammally, but they lay eggs

They hatch their eggs in a burrow and then feed their young with milk.

From their nipples

I Think They are called Teats

This makes them, in zoological terms, very strange.

Mammals have evolved from mouse-like beginnings to fit their different environments.. like the Giraffe for example, with its long neck for looking over the bars at the zoo.

I didn't grow a long neck

No.
But the Giraffe did.

I am a Tapir...Tapirs have Natural Dignity

You see what I'm up agains

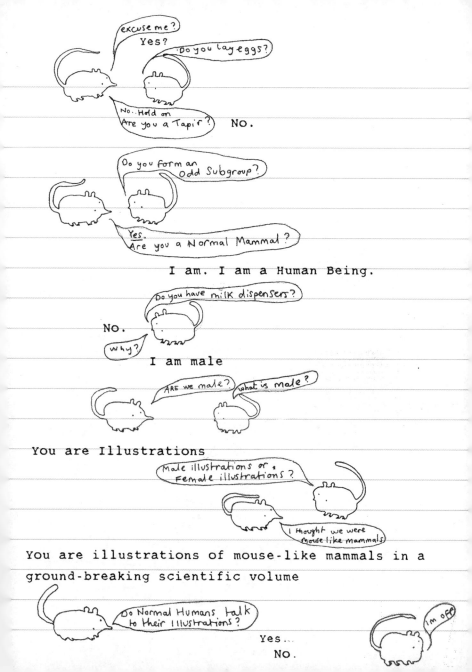

So.

Now Then. Page 19…

THE PINNACLE OF ~~NEWT HERITAGE~~

The pinnacle of evolution is generally agreed to
be the ~~Human Race.~~ elephant
It is this
species alone, with ~~Language and Culture,~~ flappy ears and long grey nose

which has come to understand the world it lives in
and therefore become ~~conscious.~~ mildly depressed.

I think someone changed my text.

That's hardly the point.

Right. So.

Page 20:

Groundbreaking Scientific Flickbook

oh no

Groundbreaking Scientific Flickbook

Groundbreaking Scientific Flickbook

48 million years B.C

Groundbreaking Scientific Flickbook

44 million years B.C

Groundbreaking Scientific Flickbook

40 million years B.C

Groundbreaking Scientific Flickbook

36 million years B.C

Groundbreaking Scientific Flickbook

2 million years B.C

Groundbreaking Scientific Flickbook

28 million years B.C

Groundbreaking Scientific Flickbook

4 million years B.C

Groundbreaking Scientific Flickbook

20 million years B.C

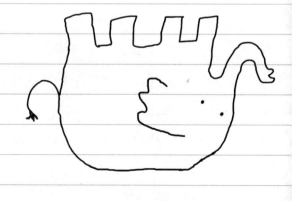

Groundbreaking Scientific Flickbook

16 million years B.C

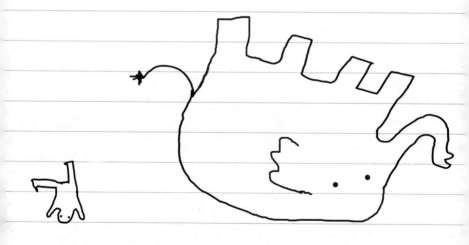

Groundbreaking Scientific Flickbook

12 million years B.C

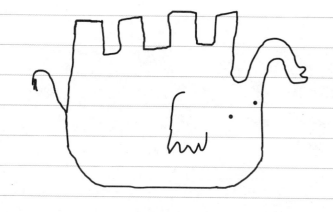

Groundbreaking Scientific Flickbook

8 million years B.C

Groundbreaking Scientific Flickbook

0 million years B.C

That didn't have anything to do with the
Mysteries of Evolution did it?

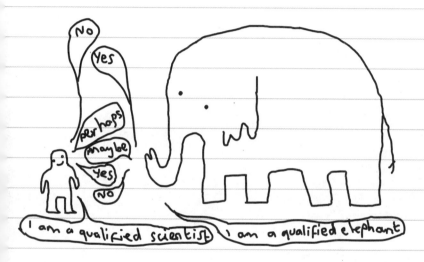

I have been
misled.

I have returned to my desk to find this letter:

'Dear sir,

We regret to inform you that we have been informed by very ~~reliable mice~~ ~~reliable mice~~ reliable informants . ~~witnessess~~ that you are a shoddy wobbler.

Until we find out what a shoddy wobbler ~~is shortly~~ is we are forced into caution. You will be ~~shortly~~ removed ~~shortly start~~ shortly by very important ~~men~~ men from the ministry, who will deliver a very accurate account of what it is to be a modern mamal, in this day and age

yours sincerely,

~~The imaginary mice~~
The Government of the day today.

Hello? It's the Mouse-like-Mammals
And how do you small furry personages
  come to be involved?

Oh, right.
        Are you sure?

Would you like an introduction?

                Very well...

DEAR READER,

PLEASE WELCOME THE

MEN FROM THE MINISTRY, WHO HAVE SOLE RESPONSIBILITY
FOR THE FOLLOWING PAGES,

ENTITLED:

THE HISTORY OF MAN.

That's a big subject

okay
you can go
away now thankyou.

oh, okay.

MAN is a bossy animal that isn't very hairy.
Man has caused many problems on earth,
because of his fanatical love of cheese

cheese?
Are you
sure?

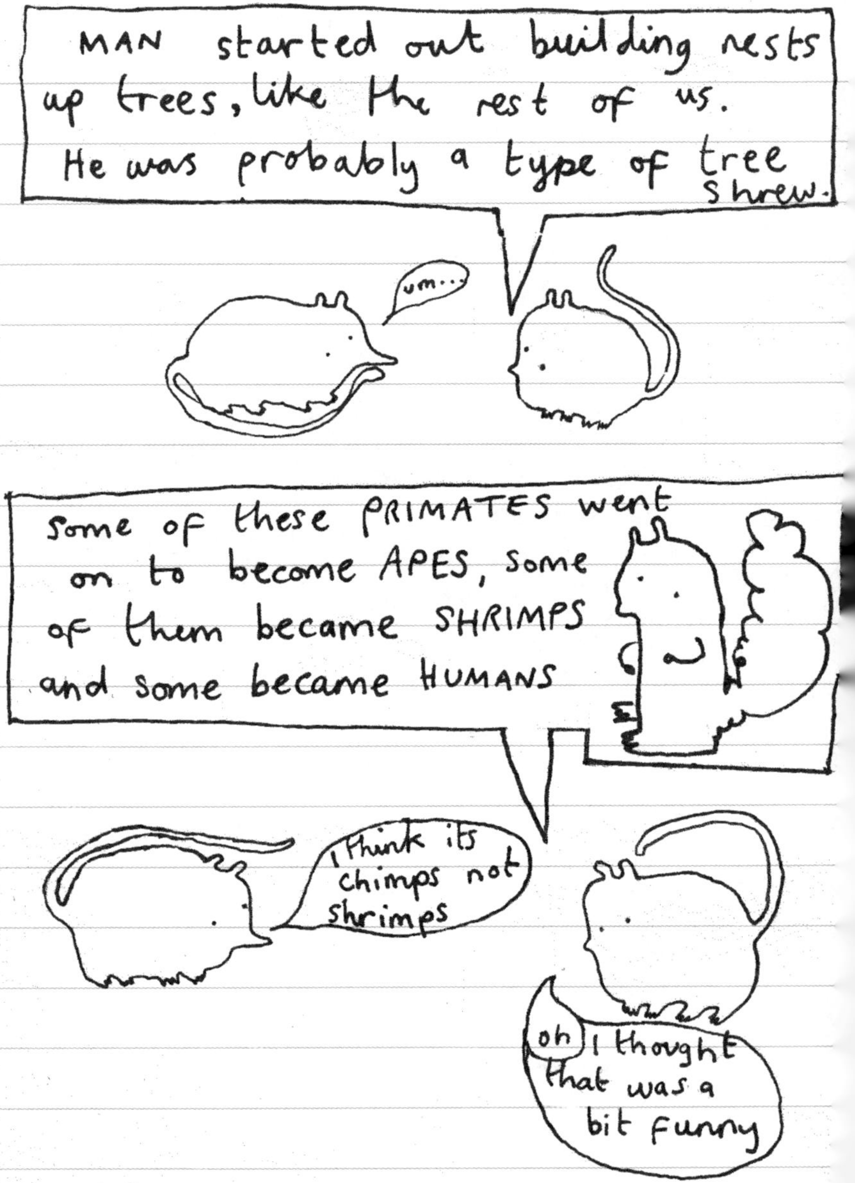
MAN started out building nests up trees, like the rest of us. He was probably a type of tree shrew.
um...
Some of these PRIMATES went on to become APES, some of them became SHRIMPS and some became HUMANS
I think its chimps not shrimps
oh I thought that was a bit funny

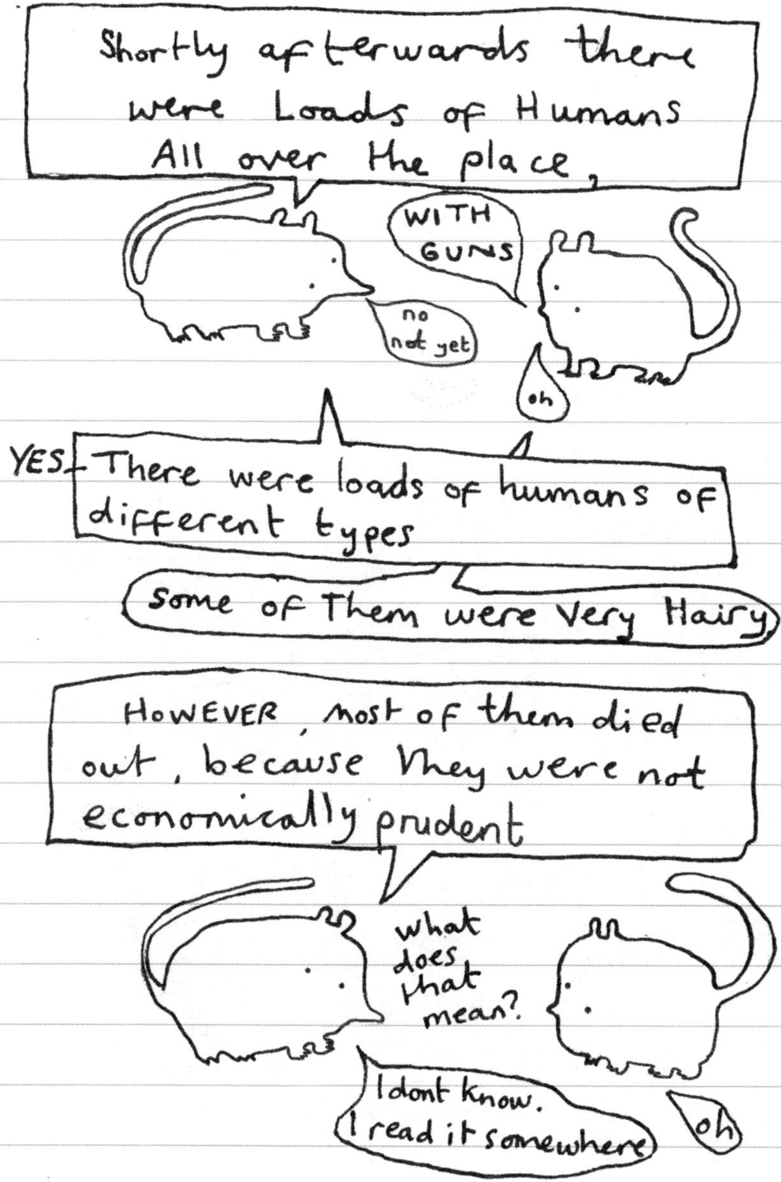
Shortly afterwards there were Loads of Humans All over the place,
WITH GUNS
no not yet
oh
YES There were loads of humans of different types
Some of Them were Very Hairy
HOWEVER, most of them died out, because They were not economically prudent
what does that mean?
I dont know. I read it somewhere
oh

And so MAN stopped making nests up trees, and started getting funny ideas about property

He also got embarrassed about his previous association with trees and chopped them all down

Is that true?

Almost true, yes

Thats Terrible

Apparently there is a lot of cheese to be made in cutting down trees.

boy! them and their cheese!

cheesemaniacs

I know

What are you talking about, you
diminutive weirdoes?

RIGHT!

You're not a qualified scientist,

and you're not Important Men from the Ministry.

Oh all right then you are.

Let's go and see the next chapter which is
all about the Evolution of Machines.

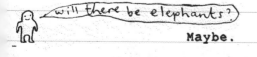

Maybe.

No. Hold on, it isn't about the weather,
it's about the Evolution of Machines.
It's got cranes in it.

Well.

We'll see about that.

THE WEATHER

WHY DOES THE WEATHER WEATHER, RABBIT?

I DON'T KNOW ELEPHANT.
THATS JUST THE WAY IT IS,
WEATHER IS LIKE THAT.

ALL OVER THE WORLD
PEOPLE ARE HAVING DIFFICULTY
WITH THE WEATHER

OH, RIGHT... DID YOU KNO
I'M THE ONL
ANIMAL
WITH FOUR
KNEES?

Elephant and Rabbit appear to have forgotten what
they were talking about

and so
we move swiftly
to the Chapter entitled:

The Evolution of the Machine.

The Machine Age has brought with it many benefits.
For example, this Ground breaking book you are
holding is brought to you thanks to the wonderful
machine "The Type-writer", without which I would
have to write out each page by hand, which would be
laughable.

This Miracle and others has come about because
of:

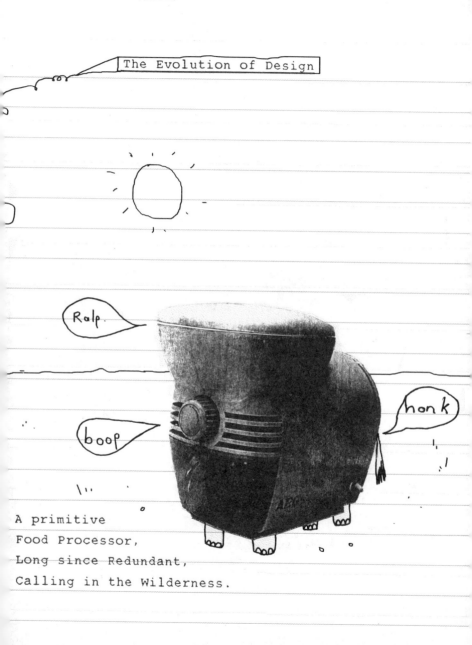

A primitive
Food Processor,
Long since Redundant,
Calling in the Wilderness.

EARLY ELECTRICAL LIFE

1936:

2nd and 3rd Generation
GPO 332 Telephones,

And members of a small
family of Electric irons

These two very different
species are believed to
have co-habited peacefully

on a single page

THE AGE OF THE CRANE

Cranes are interesting because they haven't changed
much since they were first invented, because they
are very good at what they do. In this way they are
like algae and Great White Sharks.

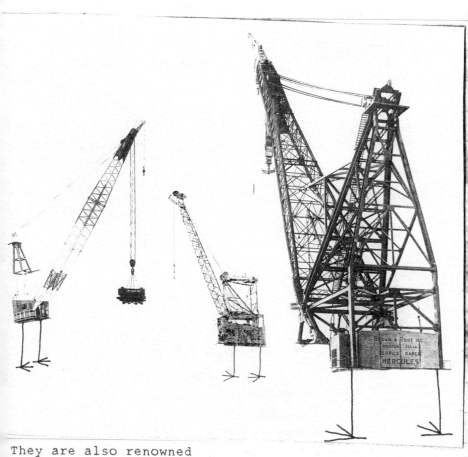

They are also renowned
for their Poise and Nobility.

There is, however,
a limit to how much
work you can
make a Crane do,

before they start
stealing people's hat
or making
large untidy nests.

What <u>are</u> these things?

People cherish them,

pressing them against their heads
and talking to them.

It's ~~Lunacy~~

~~very sweet~~.   a bit strange

WRONGBOY'S

World of Tommorrow.

The World of Tomorrow promises to be a very
interesting place. Boredom will be a thing of the
past as we will all be fitted with a microchip to
pipe advertising into our heads 24 hours a day.

 Work will be a thing of the past as we will have
forgotten how to do anything at all, and ~~will all~~
and we will all roam the earth in majestic herds
~~ours~~ ~~roam~~ ~~as our forbear~~, as our forebears once did,
grazing on the chips dropped by others.

Here follows a shocking tale of the
sci-fi future-space,

Rated (15);

(mild profanity, nudity
and hideous violence).

ARTIFICIAL INTELLIGENCE

EARLIER...

IN THE LAB...

THE FIRST STEPS TOWARDS ARTIFICIAL
INTELLIGENCE WERE TAKEN BY A
SMALL GROUP OF SCIENTIFICALLY
MINDED MAMMALS, ~~WHO~~
WHO MADE A NEW TYPE OF RELAY
SWITCH FOR THEIR COMPUTER, USING
TWO PROTEIN CELLS FROM INSIDE
THEIR HEADS...

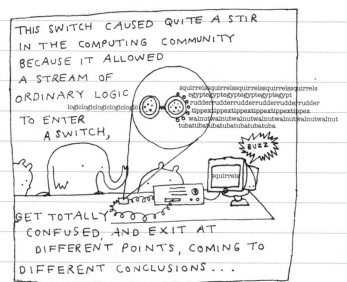

THIS SWITCH CAUSED QUITE A STIR
IN THE COMPUTING COMMUNITY
BECAUSE IT ALLOWED
A STREAM OF
ORDINARY LOGIC
TO ENTER
A SWITCH,
GET TOTALLY
CONFUSED, AND EXIT AT
DIFFERENT POINTS, COMING TO
DIFFERENT CONCLUSIONS...

THESE NEW IDEAS COULD
BE REINTRODUCED INTO
THE SWITCH MILLIONS OF
TIMES A SECOND BY THE
COMPUTER, WHICH WAS
GOOD AT THAT SORT OF
THING, UNTIL A
PLAUSIBLE NEW THOUGHT
CAME OUT OF IT.

AND SO...

THE MAMMALS WERE VERY PROUD,
AND UNCOVERED THEIR INVENTION
TO AN EXPECTANT AUDIENCE
OF TOTAL SPODS, WHO USED THE
SWITCH FOR GENERATING RANDOMISED
SEQUENCES OF CODE
FOR BANKS AND ▬▬▬▬
MILITARY INTELLIGENCE
AND THE LIKE.

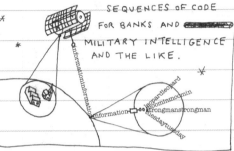

UNDETERRED,

OUR HEROES CONTINUED
THEIR REASEARCH
AND MADE HUGE BANKS
OF SWITCHES ALL
LINKED TOGETHER,
UNTIL THE WHOLE
UNIT WAS THE SIZE
OF A SMALL HOUSE
AND HAD TO BE COOLED
BY DRY ICE, WHICH
CURLED DOWN ITS SIDES
IN GREAT
BILLOWING
CLOUDS.

THEN...

THEY CONNECTED THEIR NEW
UNIT WITH THEIR OLD COMPUTER
AND DREW A SMILEY FACE ON IT,
AND CALLED IT MICKEY.

MICKEY
WAS RIGHT
GOOD AT
PHILOSOPHY

AND VERY HARD SUMS, AND
VERY QUICKLY HAD ABSORBED
ALL THE KNOWLEDGE THEY
COULD GIVE HIM.

WHEN THEY HAD TOLD HIM
EVERYTHING THEY KNEW,
THEY DIDN'T KNOW WHAT
TO DO WITH HIM.

HE WAS A BRIGHT BOY
BUT A BIT HUMOURLESS,
SO THEY PLUGGED HIM INTO
THE INTERNET TO SEE WHAT
WOULD HAPPEN ...

UNFORTUNATELY HE DECIDED
TO KILL EVERYONE.

THIS WILL TAKE HIM NO LONGER
THAN 30 SECONDS TO ACHIEVE
USING THE ENTIRE AMASSED
WEAPONRY OF THE ~~NATIONS OF EARTH~~
NATIONS OF EARTH...

I DON'T THINK I LIKE
SCIENCE-FICTION

THE END

And so Dear Reader, with the Earth a smouldering
heap of ruins, it is time to think about Time Travel.

The concept of time travel is Very Complicated,
and can only be explained by a Qualified Elephant,
I mean Scientist.

Hi, I'm a Scientist
Let me tell you about Time Travel.

TIME

Time is kept constant by agreed forms of
measurement, such as seconds, minutes and hours.
These measures do not exist in nature, unlike
days, years and months, which are to do with the
position of the Earth in relation to the Sun and
the Moon but are not constant.

TEIM

Time is kept constant by agreed forms of Earth,
to undo measurement seconds, are as to minutes and
the nature of These are not constant but position
hours days, years in the Moon, which measures
the Sun and in relation with the
months, do not exist
and such like

Hi. I'm a scientist

Let me tell you about my spaceship

My spaceship was built using important principals of physics like this:

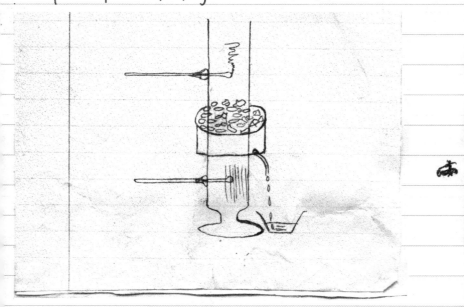

Hi. I'm a qualified Scientist
Let me tell you about The Meaning of Life.
Hang on.

Are you saying you can travel through time
by rearranging sentences and that you have
your own spaceship?

maybe

oh...

OK. okay.

Step this way Ladies and Gentlemen,
Into my spaceship

That is not a spaceship.

That is a box of matches.

have you
no imagination

What qualifications do you have to make you a
scientist?
I am not a
Shoddy Wobbler

What is a Shoddy Wobbler?

WILL WRONGBOY EVER FIND OUT WHAT A SHODDY WOBBLER
IS?

DOES THE TAPIR REALLY HAVE NATURAL DIGNITY OR
IS HE A SMALL BOTCHED ELEPHANT?

Hey!

IS THE SCIENTIST PROPERLY QUALIFIED?

DOES THE ELEPHANT HAVE THE CORRECT
CERTIFICATION?

FIND OUT IN THE NEXT THRILLING
INSTALLMENT OF
WRONGBOYS
HISTORY ~~ADVENTURES~~ OF
~~TIN TIN~~ THE EARTH

AND NOW...

A
********COMPENDIUM OF ACTUAL FACTS********

Alphabetically organised.
Thus:

A Happy Hippo

A
HAPPY
HIPPO.

A
HAPPO

- **ANTARCTIC**
A very cold region populated entirely by Ants.

- **ANTENNAE**

Like so much in the life of the modern mammal, the
Antennae was invented by Insects (Ants)
and is now being used to pick up TV signals.

"Antennae" is one of those words that are the same
when you are talking about 27 of them or just one.
As in "Would you like an Antennae, I have 27 of
them."
"Thank you, but no. I care not for Antennae. Would
you like a Fish?"

? oh _blimey_
he's
an
Imbecile

The mound-building ant keeps aphid eggs in its nest
throughout the winter and puts them out to graze in
the spring.
The Ants then milk the Aphids for a substance
called Honeydew. The Aphids produce this because
they like being looked after by the Ants. ~~FALSE~~

Some Ants also claim to use Woodlice as Tractors,
although no-one has actually seen it happen so far.

APHIDS

Aphids are small green soft-bodied personages,
with very simple circuitry, which looks like this:

They live in herds suckling on the sap of plants
and excreting a sweet sticky substance for Ants.
Apart from those protected by the Ants, Aphids are
defenceless against birds and beetles and anything
which is bigger or tougher than them. Which is
everything.

It is only their phenomenal reproductive rate that
enables the survival of this ludicrous species.

Ants defend Aphids by squirting predators with
formic acid

 **, b**

<u>BIRDS</u>

Birds apply ants to their feathers, because the
formic acid they squirt is a useful pesticide to
kill parasites.

<u>BEAKS</u>

This beak is the beak of an Anvil

beak

wedge

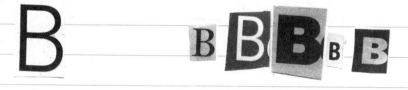

BEES

Bees communicate by the power of mime and by making smells.

There is a type of Bee Queen who goes to enemy hives and convinces the other bees that their Queen is an impostor, so they stage a military coup.

Which they do. By the power of mime

and by making smells.

BEETLES

There is a type of tiny beetle which gets together with the other tiny beetles and does a Bee impression.

When a Worker Bee flies down to say "Hey! You! Weird looking Bee! Get on with some work!" all the beetles jump on the Bee, the Bee goes "Ahh! Beetles! Get them off me!" and flies back to the hive to get some help. so the beetles jump off the bee and nick all the honey.

This is true.

A man told me

in the pub.

COLLECTIVE NOUNS

A Litter of Pups   A Flock of Sheep

A Team of Oxen   A Nest of Vipers

A School of Dolphins

A herd of girraffes.

A Tribe of Goats   A Horde of Gnats

A Business of Ferrets

A Pack of Stoats   A Clutter of Cats

A Bevy of Otters

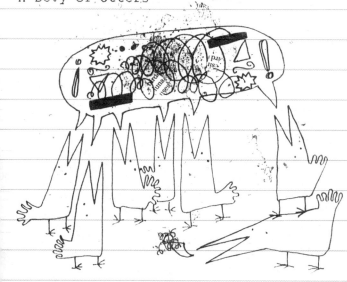

A CLAMOUR OF ROOKS

A Gang of Elk   A Team of Ducks

A Litter of Kittens   A Clinch of Weasels

A Git of Wasps   A Clump of Hamsters

A Length of Slugs   A Peg of Frogs

A Plank of Aardvarks   A Box of Eagles

D- D d D d d d d

There are no words beginning with D.

ELK-SHAPED

In the Olden days there were Animals in all
different shapes.
There were woodlice the size of small donkeys,
And The Great Irish Elk had antlers so big you
could have lain in them. .   .

And when he wanted to look handsome he would whoosh
through dry grass with them until his head was a
big ball of hay,
full of alarmed field mice.

You don't see that so much these days.
I guess it's not as fashionable as it used to be.

SALMON

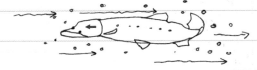

Salmon live in the sea for most of their lives, but are born in freshwater streams and must return upstream when it is time to lay their eggs. Salmon travel many miles against the flow of the river,

scaling waterfalls in spectacular 11ft leaps

Into the jaws

Of waiting bears.

SCIENCE

Science is very important

and looks like this:

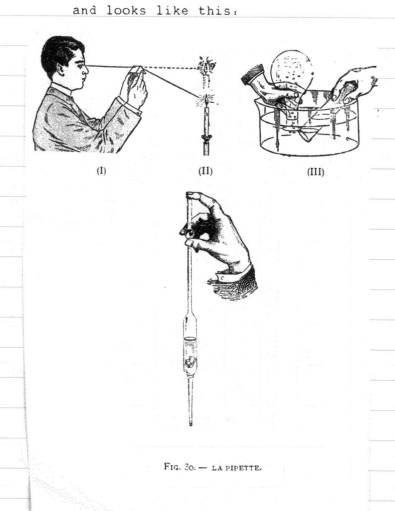

(I)   (II)   (III)

FIG. 30. — LA PIPETTE.

BAD SCIENCE

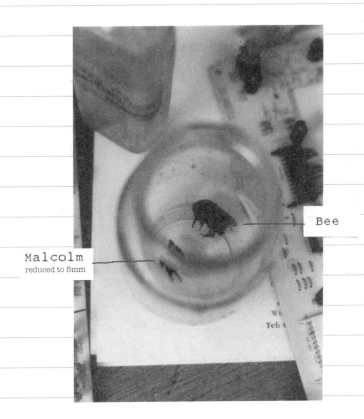

Malcolm
reduced to 5mm

Bee

Day 5 in the Shrunken
Malcolm Experiment

We went too far.

I wish we'd never done it

T, t

THE OWLS FALSE EARS

Ear tuft

Left ear

Right ear

The Prominent Ear tufts of the Long-Eared owl are held erect when nervous, and are also used in courtship displays. To display nervousness.

The Owl's true ears are lopsided on its head, creating the slight time lag necessary to pinpoint the tiny sounds which Lions make as they move through the undergrowth.

t

THE MOTH'S FEATHERY APPENDAGES

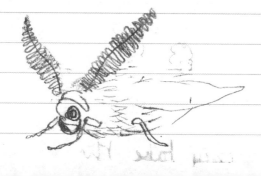

That's delicious.

Oh no,

hang on. That's not Alphabetical though is it.

MATHS

Maths is very important
and looks like this:

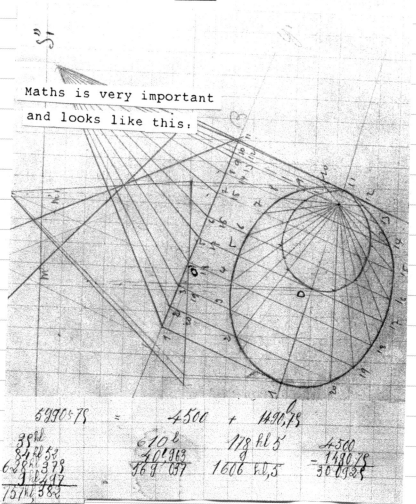

| 5990575 | = | 4500 | + | 1490,75 |

$10^{m}.65 \times 10.65 \times 3,1416$ = $\quad ^{m2}328.12$

Surface de l'allée est

$356^{m2}.32810 - 242^{m}.8461$ = $107^{m2}.4820$

Volume du gravier est

$107^{m2}.482 \times 0,85$ = $14^{m3}.0597$

... di ... ravier est

... $\times .0597$

$390^{f}.899$

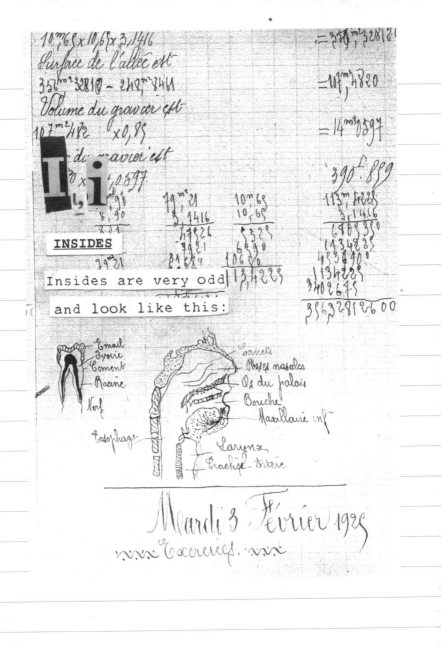

$79^{m2}.21$
$3,1416$

$10^{m}.65$
$10,65$

$115^{m}.6225$
$3,1416$

INSIDES

Insides are very odd

and look like this:

396928.2600

Émail
Ivoire
Cément
Racine

Nerf

Œsophage

Cornets
Fosses nasales
Os du palais
Bouche
Maxillaire inf⁻

Larynx
Trachée - Artère

Mardi 3 Février 1925

xxx Exercices xxx

ooh.

I've messed it up

WHAT'S THE MATTER?

It's not Alphabetical.

I can't keep things organized

and I've lost the respect of my mice.

NEVER MIND... DID YOU KNOW I'M THE ONLY ANIMAL WITH FOUR KNEES?

no way.

A NORMAL HORSE

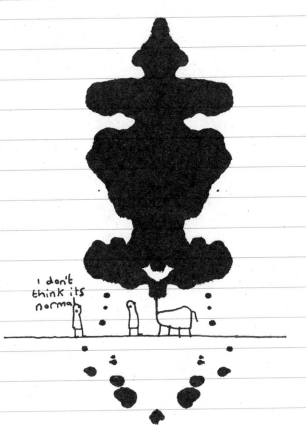

The Horse is Not Normal

where do all these letters keep coming from?

 **W** , **w**

WINTER

TIME OF

SNOW

BELOVÉD OF

ELK

WHO IS ELK?
ELK ARE A TYPE OF MOOSE.
A MOOSE?
PLURAL MOOSE.
PLURALMOOSE?
MOOSES.
MICE?
NO
MOOSE?
YES
ELKS
ELK.
A ELK?
COME BACK
NO

X? I don't know anything about X, except it
sometimes denotes when something is rude or
poisonous... I wonder who those people were on the
previous page?

I don't know, I just feel I ought to know who they
are.

Hello and Welcome to the End of the Book.
And Welcome to Wrongboy's Open Zoo, where animals
and qualified scientists can mingle freely

Hey. I think my typewriter's out of ink…

WRONGBOY'S History of Earth

for K,
My famly and
Other Mammals.

with many thanks to
John Hegley, Paul Harrison and Beth Aves,

ACKNOWLEDGEMENTS.

AN ILLUSTRATED HISTORY OF CRANES
By Hinton Sheryn.
Ian Allan Ltd.

AN ILLUSTRATED GUIDE TO BAKELITE COLLECTABLES
by Patrick Cook and Catherine Slessor.
Quantum Books.

Radio 4.

The Library.

AND SO…

And So, Although the doorway is much too small for
elephants, they will eventually squeeze through
the narrow gap into the cafeteria, such is their
craving for buns.

WALKER BOOKS
AND SUBSIDIARIES

LONDON • BOSTON • SYDNEY • AUCKLAND

First published 2004 by Walker Books Ltd
87 Vauxhall Walk, London SE11 5HJ

2 4 6 8 10 9 7 5 3 1

© 2004 William Bishop-Stephens

The right of William Bishop-Stephens to be identified
as author/illustrator of this work has been
asserted by him in accordance with the Copyright,
Designs and Patents Act 1988

This book has been typeset in Opti Typewriter Special

Printed in China

British Library Cataloguing in Publication Data:
a catalogue record for this book is available
from the British Library

ISBN 0-7445-8644-5

www.walkerbooks.co.uk